School and Family Poems

selected by Wendy Body

Contents

Wet Playtime Dave Ward   2

Two Infants Fred Sedgwick   4

The Champion Tony Charles   6

The Dinner Lady Charles Thomson   10

I'm the youngest in our house Michael Rosen   14

My Uncle Paul of Pimlico Mervyn Peake   18

Pearlie Mountblossom Helen Dunmore   20

LONGMAN

Wet Playtime

hungry chatter
friendly chatter
pitter patter
what's the matter?
tattered textbooks
skim like skates
bad boys batter
last week's mates
watch the rain
just drench the playground
blowing paper
round and round.

Here inside
the jigsaws clatter
eat those crisps
they'll make you fatter
drop your juice
and dodge the splatter
teacher's coming
quick let's scatter
pitter patter
nitter natter
friendly chatter
what's the matter?

Dave Ward

Two Infants

Paul Topple and John Randall
are friends today.
Squatting like frogs,
heads almost touching,
they stare down a drain cover
at lolly stick, leaf, or insect –
and I stand there wishing
they'd always be friends that way,
heads together, eyes watching
lolly stick, leaf, insect
down a drain cover.

Fred Sedgwick

The Champion

Step forward, Billy Green,
Pride of the school!
Billy's done it once again,
Billy's really cool.
Mornings in Assembly,
He sings the wrong tune;
But every year he's champion
At the Egg and Spoon.

Who's that training
Behind the canteen,
Pebbles balanced on a stick?
That's Billy Green:
Dodging and weaving.
Darting round about
– Serious training.
Better watch out.

Doesn't like playing Chess,
Says it hurts his brain;
Doesn't like Soccer,
Especially in the rain;
Doesn't like Cross-Country,
Says it hurts his feet;
But once a year on Sports Day,
He's the one to beat.

Look at that footwork!

Look at those legs!

Look at that dexterity,

He never breaks the eggs!

Such an egg and spoon race

Was surely never seen:

Come up here and take your prize,

Champion Billy Green.

Tony Charles

The Dinner Lady

I'm the dinner lady
serving up stew.
I'm the dinner lady
"how do you do?"

I'm the dinner lady:
"NOT SO MUCH NOISE!
Let's have a bit of quiet,
girls and boys.
Get back Peter
and wait your turn."
I don't earn much
but it's all I earn.

"Amanda, you mustn't
pick on Jane.
I've told you before –
I won't tell you again."
At home I've got
four kids of my own.
"Michael, why are you
sitting all alone?
You don't look well –
are you feeling upset?
Come over here
and tell me, my pet.

Cheer up now,
let me dry your tears."
I'm the dinner lady
and I've been here twenty years.
I get out the plates,
I stack and wash and dry,
I serve up ice cream
and apple pie.

Then, when the kids are gone
and I've swept the floor,
I put on my coat
and I walk out the door
and I go back home
and I pour a cup of tea
and I'm not the dinner lady:
Oh no! I'm ME.

Charles Thomson

I'm the youngest in our house

I'm the youngest in our house
so it goes like this:

My brother comes in and says:
"Tell him to clear the fluff
out from under his bed."
Mum says,
"Clear the fluff
out from under your bed."

Father says,
"You heard what your mother said."
"What?" I say.

"The fluff," he says.
"Clear the fluff
out from under your bed."
So I say,
"There's fluff under his bed, too,
you know."

So father says,

"But we're talking about the fluff
under *your* bed."

"You will clear it up
won't you?" mum says.

So now my brother – all puffed up –
says,

"Clear the fluff
out from under your bed,
clear the fluff
out from under your bed."

Now I'm angry. I am angry.
So I say – what shall I say?
I say,
"Shuttup Stinks
YOU CAN'T RULE MY LIFE."

Michael Rosen

My Uncle Paul of Pimlico

My Uncle Paul of Pimlico
Has seven cats as white as snow,
Who sit at his enormous feet
And watch him, as a special treat,
Play the piano upside-down,
In his delightful dressing gown;
The firelight leaps, the parlour glows,
And, while the music ebbs and flows,
They smile (while purring
    the refrains),
At little thoughts that cross
    their brains.

Mervyn Peake

Pearlie Mountblossom

Pearlie Mountblossom's lost
   her mother
she lives in a tent with her Dad
   and her brother,
the wind blew out and the tent
   blew in
and Pearlie early learned to swim,

Pearlie dreams in her tent at night
that the sails are set and the stars
    are bright
and the waves are turning over
    and over
and they show the face of
    Pearlie's mother,

Pearlie Mountblossom has
forty pounds
she keeps it safe in a hole in
the ground,
her leggings have stars on,
her dreams are sweet
though her brother is snoring
down by her feet,

Pearlie Mountblossom grows
mustard seeds
she keeps her flowerpots
clean of weeds,

her mustard blows in the
    morning wind
while Pearlie's father shaves
    and sings,

Pearlie has friends but they never
    come home,
her brother plays but he plays alone
her Dad splits kindling to make
    the fire
and the flames leap higher and
    higher and higher,

Pearlie Mountblossom's lost
    her mother
she lives in a tent with her Dad and
    her brother,
she has apples for breakfast and
    Mars Bars for tea
and at night she sails the
    whispering sea.

Helen Dunmore